LBJ Lampooned

Cartoon Criticism of Lyndon B. Johnson

With an Introduction by **Jules Feiffer**

Edited by Sig Rosenblum and Charles Antin

COBBLE HILL PRESS, INC.   NEW YORK   1968

Distributed by Hill & Wang, Inc.

LBJ
Lampooned

Cartoon Criticism of Lyndon B. Johnson

Contents

Introduction   7

LBJ and Vietnam   15

LBJ and Dissent   43

LBJ and The Great Society   59

LBJ and the Presidential Style   67

LBJ and the Credibility Gap   93

Assorted Assaults   105

Be not intimidated, therefore, by any terrors, from publishing with the utmost freedom whatever can be warranted by the laws of your country; nor suffer yourselves to be wheedled out of your liberty by any pretenses of politeness, delicacy, or decency. These, as they are often used, are but three different names for hypocrisy, chicanery, and cowardice.

—John Adams
Second President of the United States

Introduction
by
Jules Feiffer

I

Character libel is a long-established and honorable tradition in the political cartoon. In 1831 the English magazine *The Athenaeum* described the political cartoonist as—

> a man who closes his heart against the sensibilities of human nature .... who insults inferiority of mind and exposes defects of body.... who aggravates what is already hideous and blackens what was before sufficiently dark....

Use this as a gauge against current work on Lyndon Johnson and it is immediately apparent how far most of us still have to go.

In their day Gillray was the scandal of George III's monarchy, Daumier was tossed into jail by Louis-Philippe, Nast was offered a small fortune to get lost by Boss Tweed, the Wilson administration tried Art Young for conspiracy; a cartoonist once counted for something. The secret ingredient was hate. Not personal hate, but professional hate: the intensity of conviction that comes to a craftsman's work when he has made the decision to kill; a commitment to shun all political and behavioral complexities, so that the subject becomes, for example, not an overburdened leader struggling tragically with the agony of power, but purely and simply, a demon.

A blackmailer's savvy for his victim enters the artist's work— an insight so correct and damning that the drawings take on a separate life of their own, becoming psychic *doppelgänger* of the leader caricatured. The mark of their effectiveness is that to the eye of the observer the features of the real man reshape themselves to resemble more strongly their caricature. There can be no serious question that Gillray's caricatures bear a truer likeness to George III than his official portraits, and the same must be true of Daumier's Louis-Philippe and Nast's Tweed, as well as many of the other rancidly inspired cartoons between that time and this.

For that time was a pre-Marxian, pre-Freudian, pre-RANDian time. No defender of British imperialism felt the need to legitimize his position by stating: "None of us likes this war, but we are bound by a commitment to defend the freedom of the North American people. Once we lose Philadelphia, Boston goes. Once we lose Boston, Canada goes. Once we lose Canada, Ireland goes." No dissenter from the Spanish-American War was cautioned by the government to quiet his dissent lest he lend aid and comfort to Madrid.

If the work in our time shows less hate, it is not because we have lost the capacity; it is because undisguised hate is currently less marketable. Debate today is conducted on what is thought of as a more responsible level: meaning, simply, that when the press uncovers the irresponsible truth, it is denied. A lust for conquest was not in the past considered a moral deficiency as it now (officially) is, and open opposition to war once carried with it more danger than it does today. Hate is a luxury of the illiterate and the insular. Once literacy and mass communications enter our lives we have to be a lot more cautious in admitting what our real aims are, and who it is we want to kill.

When people say that issues today are so complex that it is impossible to tell right from wrong, what they are really saying is that they are getting more news about themselves than they like, and that they *can* tell but they don't want to. This avoidance of the unpalatable has come to be known as good taste. With tastefulness so prominent a feature in our make-up it is to Lyndon Johnson's credit that he has single-handedly undone the evasiveness developed over the last fifty years and restored open vitriol to a place of honor in our land. The high passions aroused by the President's conduct of his office, and in particular the War in Vietnam, have returned us to a simpler (one might even say preliterate) stage of American history.

II

"I hope the day will never arrive when I shall neither be the object of calumny or ridicule, for then I shall be neglected and forgotten," said Johnson, the Doctor, not the President. "Have you heard the British demean their king or queen?...You don't demean the ruler," answers Everett McKinley Dirkson some time later.

There are charitable ways of describing Lyndon Johnson. They will not be found in this volume. As noted earlier, the political cartoon is not at its best when trying to be fair. It is at its best when trying to be cruel. Fortunate to the service of truth—in the case of the President—to be fair is to be cruel. He has, since Vietnam, been a hostile cartoonist's dream. Defenders of the President claim that what his critics really have against him is his style. Ordinarily it would be enough. But the Johnson style as we know it today is very different from the Johnson style we used to know. In his earliest days in office the President was seen as a Rooseveltian figure, later as a brilliant political strategist, later as the nation's number one civil-rights leader, later as a man who was touched by his own childhood poverty to the extent that he intended to see all poverty wiped out in his lifetime. He was so good, he was lousy for cartoonists.

First of all, he is not all that easy to draw. An overabundance of oversized features makes caricature difficult, makes friendly caricature damned near impossible. It is beyond ordinary talent to do a drawing of Johnson that looks like Johnson and, at the same time, make him look honest. However well disposed one might have once been to the President, his eyes could never be described as warm, or (as in the case of Kennedy whose eyes were not warm either) touched with humor; and the set of his mouth bears an unfortunate resemblance to that of the man at the bank who turns down your loan. Now, if you have drawn a man with small, pouchy eyes, and a tight mouth set inside a flushed face that inclines toward puffiness, what you have drawn is a well-to-do drunk. Not the image one was after at all. So most early Johnson drawings were inadequate. The resemblance was scanty. For humor they focused on the President's whirlwind vitality, his use of the telephone, his careless driving, his passion for turning out lights in the White House, his Texas manner.

Amusing, and at times no doubt annoying to the President, but hardly lethal. Style only became a problem to Johnson after he won as a peace candidate and promptly went to war. And the problem was not one of style so much as one of identity. Before the policy of escalation we didn't know who the President really was. We have since found out. We have come to see him as not vital but violent, not clever but devious, not shrewd but cynical, not political but hypocritical, not populist but paranoic. He is less John Wayne in the White House (as popular mythology would have it) than he is Victor Jory. Or to put the movie metaphor in its proper context: if Richard Nixon reminds us of the man who sells whiskey to the Indians, Lyndon Johnson reminds us of the man who has sold the whiskey to Nixon. Through no encouragement of our own, Johnson has developed from a poor subject for political cartoons to a glorious subject. Though World War III may be just around the corner, to the true pro these are the best times since Boss Tweed.

III

I don't care what they print about me, most of my constituents can't read anyhow—but them damn pictures!   —Boss Tweed

And how are we handling the times? Certainly better than we handled World War I. William Murrell in *A History of American Graphic Humor* writes:

In order to inform the cartoonist of the many specific subjects upon which the government wished to have cartoons drawn, the Bureau of Cartoons was established in December 1917.... The Bureau published weekly the *Bulletin for Cartoonists,* which was sent regularly to every cartoonist in the United States. These bulletins contained subjects for cartoons, as suggested by the U. S. Food Administration, the Treasury Department, and other government agencies. Thus a considerable cartoon power was developed, stimulating recruiting, popularizing the draft, saving food and fuel, selling Liberty Bonds, etc., etc. When they were not doing their utmost to graphically urge any and all of the above suggestions, the cartoonists, for the most part, concentrated their efforts on Uncle Sam buckling on armor, or the Kaiser with a bomb, pistol, or knout. There were exceptions, of course, but they are almost impossible to find.

The exceptions as it turns out were all left wing: Robert Minor, Art Young, Boardman Robinson—all publishing in *Masses*; for who else would have them? The situation today is quite different: never before in wartime have so many respectable artists in so many responsible publications gone so far out of their way to get their President. Vietnam is our most unhappy international involvement since we fought Spain, and our most internally disruptive war since 1865. Whether we attack Johnson on his tax program, his poverty program, his credibility gap, or his handling of the cities, when you get right down to it what we are all really talking about is Vietnam.

There are serious moral objections to Lyndon Johnson's involvement in Vietnam but these only trouble the peace movement. The issue that alienates the American people is that we are not winning. Lyndon Johnson has dropped more bombs per month on North Vietnam than were dropped per month on Europe and Africa in World War II, and we are not winning. He has sent nearly a half-million American troops to join 622,000 South Vietnamese troops, not to mention 45,000 South Korean troops, all million of them fighting 358,000 of the enemy, and we are not winning. He has dropped the most sophisticated explosive deviants known to man on the heads of North and South Vietnamese alike, and we are not winning. Here we have the first war in history to have its news coverage *entirely* in *color,* and we are not winning! Small reason bitterness sweeps the land. Americans are winners; we have never lost a war. *One* of us is worth *ten* of *them*—we are taught that practically from birth. (Johnson to the Senate: "There's an old saying down in Texas: if you know you are right, just keep on coming and no gun can stop you.") More basic to our national identity than the Constitution itself" is the ferocious belief that what Americans do is *win*. Well, for crying out loud, who got us into this mess in the first place? The President (ably assisted by all those officials who have access to more information than we do) has brought the country to the brink of mutiny.

So it is the fact that he is not a winner that makes us look more critically upon Lyndon Johnson. Winning is the personality trait that first recommended him to our favor: if we were to love Johnson at all it had to be for his winning. There is nothing else to admire him for: Joe McCarthy had more charm, Richard Nixon, as much sincerity, and Thomas E. Dewey, equal warmth. Or, as Joseph Alsop puts it, "The fact has to be faced that President Johnson has an uninspiring, perhaps even a downright bad moral style." We can suffer a bad moral style in victory only: when civil-rights legislation was passed, when the War on Poverty was organized, when Medicare went through, the Johnson style was discussed either defensively or affirmatively, and all good liberals hoped that the Bobby Baker case would quietly go away. What we wouldn't give to have it back with us today.

Defenders of Johnson further assert that had President Kennedy lived and made the same moves in Vietnam as his successor, he would not be subjected to the same sort of villification. They are undoubtedly right—which goes to prove how fortunate, in this case, to have at long last a president whose style coincides with his content. Kennedy could possibly have convinced us that Vietnam was a just war, and a whole generation of young people, hypnotized by charisma, could possibly have marched proudly off to napalm and defoliate, knowing that their country stood firmly behind them—a far more frightening national image than today's. Give me a nation of draft resisters anytime.

So we do owe Johnson something. Compare the early Levine drawing of Johnson weeping crocodile tears to the later Levine drawing of a crocodile weeping Johnson tears and you will see how far recent experiences have deepened us.

IV

He moved in close, his face a scant millimeter from his target, his eyes widening and narrowing, his eyebrows rising and falling. From his pockets poured clippings, memos, statistics.
—Rowland Evans and Robert Novak,
Lyndon B. Johnson: The Exercise of Power

He picked his nose. He was liable, when slumped down in his chair, to reach casually and unashamedly into his groin to ease his pants.... To a reporter who began an interview with a trivial question, he said, "Why do you come and ask me, the leader of the Western world, a chicken-shit question like that?"
—Michael Davie, *LBJ: A Foreign Observer's Viewpoint*

Johnson had compromised too many contradictions and now the contradictions were in his face: when he smiled, the corners of his mouth squeezed gloom; when he was pious, his eyes twinkled irony; when he spoke in a righteous tone, he looked corrupt; when he jested, the ham in his jowls looked to quiver. He was not convincing.
—Norman Mailer, *Cannibals and Christians*

The above quotations indicate to some extent the difficulty in dealing graphically with the President: how is it possible to overdo? The degree of restraint practiced by several in this volume is, by one's own lights, either admirable or chicken. The degree of excess is, by one's own lights, either accurate or offensive. Mauldin's Johnson is the most human and, to me, therefore, the least appealing. Szep, Macpherson, and Franklin go to the other extreme: put their three Johnsons behind a bubbling pot (labeled "Congress" or "Vietnam" or " '68 elections") and you have the witches in *Macbeth*. Conrad's Johnson would be natural sitting across a collective-bargaining table from Haynie's Johnson: Jimmy Hoffa talking terms with Roger Blough. There is a smattering of cowboy Johnsons; the less said about them the better. Levine's Johnson is pure bitter-soul; the Johnson that, of all others, I would happily trade my own for. My own is taken from the Norman Mailer model described above.

And how goes the campaign? I have no idea how it goes with my colleagues, but in my case I have been assaulting the President since March of 1965, and he isn't out of Vietnam, he isn't in the ghettos, and he's switched from chanting "We Shall Overcome" at Negro universities to addressing National Police-Chief Conventions on the need for Law and Order.

Not that I'm not being listened to. After the Newark and Detroit uprisings I drew a bloated-looking President appointing a fact-finding commission which included one Democrat, one Republican, one intellectual, one anti-intellectual, one young person, one old person, one Negro, and one bigot. The last panel had the President smiling his falsest smile and saying, "Come, let us reason together."

The White House requested the original.

Talk about effectiveness.

LBJ and Vietnam

Men...may talk of patriotism; they may draw a few examples from ancient story, of great achievements performed by its influence; but whoever builds upon it, as a sufficient Basis for conducting a long and bloody War, will find themselves deceived in the end. I do not mean to exclude altogether the Idea of Patriotism. I know it exists, and I know it has done much in the present Contest. But I will venture to assert, that a great and lasting War can never be supported on this principle alone. It must be aided by a prospect of Interest or some reward. For a time, it may, of itself push Men to Action; to bear much, to encounter difficulties; but it will not endure unassisted by Interest.

—George Washington from Valley Forge, 1778

Anybody who commits the land power of the United States on the continent of Asia ought to have his head examined.

—General Douglas MacArthur

IN FEBRUARY OF 1965, IN ORDER TO GET HANOI TO THE NEGOTIATING TABLE, WITH HEAVY HEART I ORDERED MY BOMBERS TO STRIKE NORTH VIETNAM.

THIS STRATEGY PROVED IN MANY WAYS SUCCESSFUL. BUT IT DID NOT GET HANOI TO THE NEGOTIATING TABLE.

IN JULY OF 1966, IN ORDER TO GET HANOI TO THE NEGOTIATING TABLE, WITH SOMBRE DISMAY I ORDERED MY BOMBERS TO STRIKE HANOI AND HAIPHONG.

THIS STRATEGY PROVED IN MANY WAYS EFFECTIVE. BUT IT DID NOT GET HANOI TO THE NEGOTIATING TABLE.

IN JANUARY OF 1967, IN ORDER TO GET HANOI TO THE NEGOTIATING TABLE, WITH MANIFEST SOBRIETY I ORDERED MY BOMBERS TO TAKE OUT CHINA'S NUCLEAR CAPABILITY.

THIS STRATEGY PROVED IN MANY WAYS FRUITFUL. BUT IT DID NOT GET HANOI TO THE NEGOTIATING TABLE.

IN JULY OF 1967, IN ORDER TO GET HANOI TO THE NEGOTIATING TABLE, WITH THE AGONY OF POWER I ORDERED MY BOMBERS TO STRIKE PEKING.

NOW, AT THIS VERY MOMENT, MY MISSILES ARE RELUCTANTLY ALERTED FOR MOSCOW.

LET ME WARN HANOI —

MY RESTRAINT IS NOT INEXHAUSTIBLE.

JULES FEIFFER

"Wheeee....!"

"How can I put it in a face-saving way?"

"Watch out!—Here comes our bit now…"

The family that preys together.

"Premier Ky sent us as observers to guarantee the fairness
of the 1968 presidential elections."

"Cheer up Lyndon, I'm with you 100 percent on Vietnam"

"Ya see, Joe, the important thing is, they gotta figure out
a way to save the President's face."

"Allow me to introduce an old friend of mine..."

"Well, what do you say now!!?"

"$34 per head is a mighty handsome sum, Ma'am, considering
what it cost to kill him in the first place..."

"People ask me who my heroes are. I have only one—Hitler."

"...You're getting war-weary...very war-weary..."

"That's for nothing, now DO something."

"Red China come into the war if we bomb the China-North
Vietnam border?...Nonsense!"

Time Machine

"Free elections will be held in South Vietnam in: (a) six months (b) one year   (c) five years   (d) never."

"Yes, operator, I'm still here…"

LBJ and Dissent

Heresies are necessary for the philosophical and theological health of a culture.

—Miguel de Unamuno

... And with Lyndon Johnson I have argued, fought and debated on the floor, in his office and my office, but we can still call each other friends. It is only when we allow disagreement to overrun and overrule good judgment that we forget our basic goodness and decency in this country.

—Barry Goldwater

One man alone within his conscience—whether in the laboratory or the study or the classroom or on the street corner—is to be jealously guarded from the thousand who, believing him wrong, would deny his right to search and his right to speak the truth.

—Lyndon B. Johnson

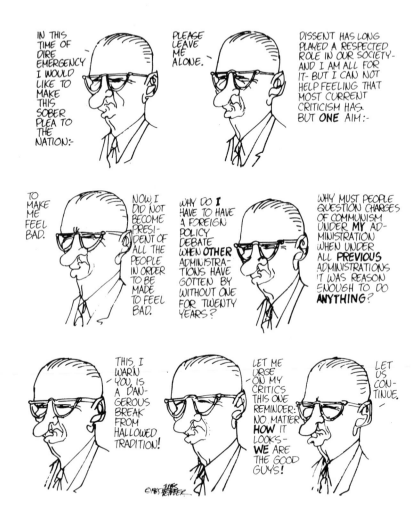

"Ah ain't no nervous Nellie…"

"Add one more military target in Hanoi…Harrison Salisbury."

"Of course, we respect the right to dissent—
if any traitors want to."

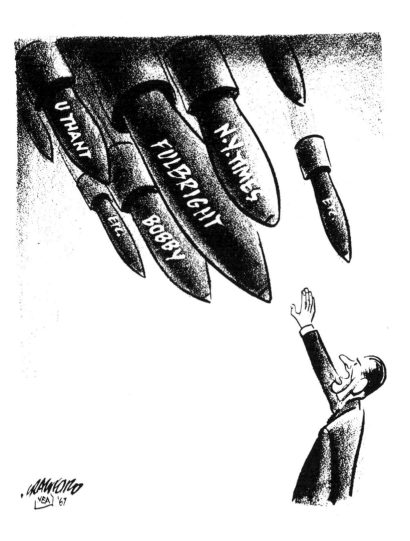

"Stop the bombing!"

"We musn't push it, Dean, but if it happens to fall in, let's cover it quick."

"And y'all kill that rumor that I'm stifling dissent in the name
of patriotism."

"I like to get out and press the flesh...!"

"How dare you...!"

"Heel!"

"Your professor said this!... Your professor said that!...
Luci, doggone it, I'm tired of what your professor said!!"

The cold line

"Schucks—we ain't feudin', are we, ol buddy?"

LBJ and the Great Society

Macbird:
... This land will be a garden carefully pruned.
   We'll lop off any branch that looks too tall,
   That seems to grow too lofty or too fast.
   And any weed that springs up on our soil,
   To choke the plants I've neatly set in rows,
   Gets plucked up root and all, by me,
       Macbird—
   And this I do for you, my wholesome flowers.
   I see a garden blooming undisturbed
   Where all the buds are even in their rows.
   An ordered garden, sweet with unity,
   That is my dream, my Smooth Society.

—MACBIRD by Barbara Garson

Prize bull or bum steer?

...For these gifts we are about to receive...

"Please understand **MY** position—it takes real guts to do this."

LBJ and the Presidential Style

Nobody but the Americans could have invented a President who poses as a peasant to conceal the expert ruthlessness that conceals the fact that he is a peasant all the time.

—James Cameron

I don't think I have the disposition, the training, or the temperament for the presidency.

—Lyndon B. Johnson

Johnson always has said he was an admirer of Roosevelt, but we thought it was Franklin rather than Teddy.

—R. H. Shackford

FIRST
THE
NEGROES
REVOLTED.

THEN THE
**PUERTO
RICANS**
REVOLTED.

BUT PUNITIVE
MEASURES ARE
NOT ENOUGH.
THESE
TROUBLED
TIMES **CRY
OUT** FOR
NEW —
ANSWERS
TO UNSOLVED
OLD PROB-
LEMS.

TO SEEK OUT
THE **CAUSES**
OF ANARCHY
AND PROPOSE
A **CURE**
I HAVE —
THIS DAY
APPOINTED
A **FACT
FINDING
COMISSION.**

"Why cain't we-all understand our fellow human beings?"

"I plan for all of Southeast Asia, a Great Society...!"

FIRST, THE EYES –

WARM. SYMPA- THETIC. THE EYES OF A MAN WHO LOVES PEOPLE.

NEXT, THE NOSE. FORTH- RIGHT. DYNAMIC. THE NOSE OF A MAN WHO'S A WINNER.

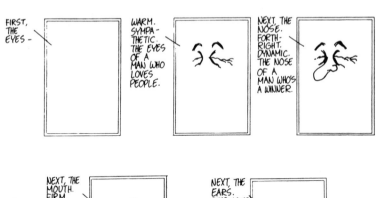

NEXT, THE MOUTH. FIRM. RESOLUTE. THE MOUTH OF A MAN WHO TELLS IT LIKE IT IS.

NEXT, THE EARS. RESPONSIVE. GENEROUS. THE EARS OF A MAN WHO LISTENS TO HIS NATION'S HEART- BEAT.

NOW FOR THE OUT- LINE. STRONG. GOOD HUMORED. THE FACE OF A MAN BELOVED TO HIS FELLOW COUNTRY- MEN.

THAT'S THE UGLIEST THING I EVER SAW.

DO IT RIGHT THIS TIME.

"I can't even fool *some* of the people *some* of the time
any more."

A finger in every sticky pie

AS YOUR PRESENT PRESIDENT — IT IS INCUMBENT UPON ME TO PLAY A VARIETY OF ROLES IN THE COURSE OF A SINGLE DAY.

POLICEMAN TO THE WORLD. —

SOCIAL WORKER TO THE POOR. —

LOVER OF PEACE. —

SEEKER OF CONSENSUS. —

EDUCATOR —

CIVIL RIGHTS LEADER. —

AT THE CLOSE OF DAY — WHAT A RELIEF IT IS TO BE ABLE TO GIT IN MY PAJAMAS —

AND JUST BE MYSELF.

"A Senator Fulbright to see you Sire. Seems he can't reconcile himself to your infallibility."

"I haven't really lost touch with you—the people—have I?"

"I don't see myself as a latter-day **FDR**. Rather, he's more an early-day me…!"

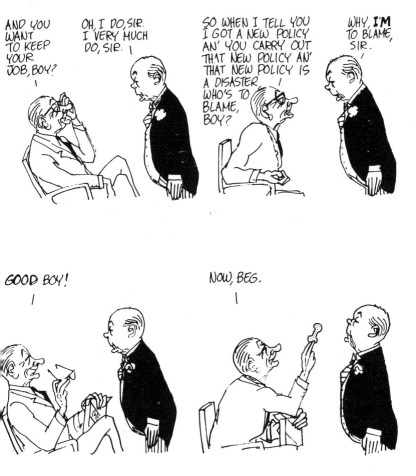

"That's a mirror, Mr. President...the portrait's over here..."

Presidential pot

"Expect no miracles...!"

The State of the Union

LBJ and the Credibility Gap

It is said that the old Chesapeake & Ohio barge canal, which runs from Washington to the mountains of Maryland, is bounded by the Cumberland Gap at one end and the Credibility Gap at the other.

Not long ago, White House correspondents devised what they called the LBJ Credibility Test. It went like this: 'When the President smoothes down the hair on the back of his head, he's telling the truth; when he strokes the side of his nose, he's telling the truth; when he rubs his hands, he's telling the truth; but when he starts moving his lips, he's lying.'

—William McGaffin and Irwin Knoll

"A usually unreliable source said today..."

"I'll order the escalation. You issue a denial to the press, and you think up a new name for it when they find out."

Lies, my dear boy, are found out immediately, because they are of two sorts. There are lies that have short legs, and lies that have long noses. Your lie, as it happens, is one of those that have a long nose.

—Pinocchio by Carlo Collodi

"In the highest traditions of American journalism—you'll be given all the news that's print to fit, I mean...fit to print."

"The question is, Mr. President, which of us is on the mainland?"

"I have no knowledge of any (hee! hee!) peace feelers, but I'd be (tee! hee!) tickled to death if they existed."

Assorted Assaults

I am the most denounced man in the world.
                              —Lyndon B. Johnson, 1965

ONE DAY A LITTLE BOY WENT TO SEE THE EMPEROR ON PARADE AND SAW RIDING, GRINNING, AND WAVING IN A BUBBLE DOMED CARRIAGE A GIANT OF A MAN WHO WAS STARK NAKED.

"WHY" EXCLAIMED THE LITTLE BOY, " THE EMPEROR HAS **NO** CLOTHES!"

TO THIS A THIRD WISE MAN ADDED, "WHETHER OR NOT THE EMPEROR SHOULD HAVE GONE INTO THE STREET WITHOUT CLOTHES IS NOW MERELY A DEBATER'S POINT. THE FACT IS THAT HE IS THERE, AND WE ARE COMMITTED."

WHEREUPON ALL THE WISE MEN CALLED FOR UNITY IN THE FACE OF DIVISIVENESS WHILE REMINDING THEMSELVES OF THE IMPORTANCE OF TOLERATING THE LITTLE BOY'S DISSENT.

TO WHICH A WISE MAN REPLIED, "WHILE IT IS **JUST** CRITICISM TO QUARREL WITH THE EMPEROR IN HIS **TASTE** IN CLOTHES, IT IS **IRRESPONSIBLE** CRITICISM TO SAY HE IS NAKED BECAUSE THAT APPROACH FAILS TO OFFER AN ALTERNATIVE."

"BESIDES," SAID A SECOND WISE MAN, "HOW CAN YOU BE SO SURE THAT THE EMPEROR DOESN'T HAVE ACCESS TO MATERIAL THAT WE DON'T HAVE? WHAT YOU'RE **REALLY** OBJECTING TO IS **STYLE!**"

OR, AS THE EMPEROR WHO HAD TAPPED THE DIALOGUE WAS TO LATER PUT IT, "ONLY IN AN ATMOSPHERE OF FREE DEBATE CAN WE DETERMINE THE FACTS."

© 1966 JULES FEIFFER

MORAL: THE EMPEROR HAS CLOTHES, YOU BETTER BELIEVE IT.

"Who said they don't like Yanks!"

Aye, yi, yi, yi!

"I'm pleased to meet you too, Mr. President, but I'm part
of your bodyguard."

"...And in exchange for Bissell, how'd the University of Toronto
like a Harvard man?"

"Just remember... I'm an independent deliberative body!"

"…The next time you abbreviate 'Stop Our Bombing'…smile!"

The Sleepwalkers

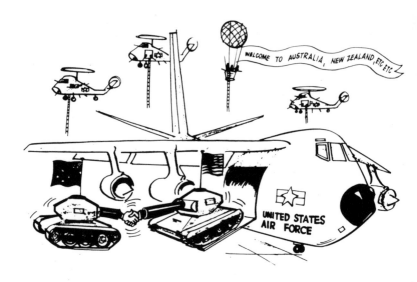

"President Johnson, I presume."

"Howdy, folks!"

"Us…"

PERMIT MOST HUMBLE UNWORTHY PERSON TO INTRODUCE HIMSELF—

THE YELLOW PERIL!

AFTER WORLD WAR II I REAPPEARED SO—WAS, ONCE AGAIN, INSCRUTABLY, CHINESE.

AND NOW, IN MYSTERIOUS WAYS OF EAST, I HAVE REACHED MOST SOPHISTICATED INCARNATION OF ALL. I AM, AT ONE AND SAME TIME, CHINESE **AND** NORTH VIETNAMESE.

"The pineapples are ticking and we don't recommend
the saki wine."

"Ah, so! You-all!"

Statue of Liberty

Bonnie and Clyde

"Yea...but how about '72?"